EXPRESS YOURSELF

A CREATIVE PRAYER JOURNAL

INSPIRED BY CHARITY “THE MIME”

CHARITY LASHAI

Published by Access Agency

www.accessagencyllc.com

Printed in the United States of America

ISBN: 978-0-578-94007-6

Cover design by Russell Kirkpatrick and Access Agency LLC

Photography by John A. White Sr.

DEDICATION

I would like to dedicate this journal to my most amazingly gifted NINI (niece). Kyndal Jenkins as you shared your teenage concerns with me, it reminded me that life as a teen can be more complicated than parents are aware of. I love you more than you know. May your life blossom into everything God desires it to be.

Also a big thank you to my favorite teacher of all time, Sylvia Guszman (5th grade). You have encouraged me every single year to continue writing, even when I was not completely convinced that I could do it. Over 30 years has gone by and you are as inspiring today as you were then. May you receive abundant return for who you have been to hundreds of children over the years.

Table of Contents

9 Express Yourself: What is a Creative Prayer Journal?

18 Prayer ACTS

29 Day 1: Multiple Identities

35 Day 2: Speak Poetry

39 Day 3: A Snap of the Past

43 Day 4: The Mime Express

47 Day 5: The Mental Picture

57 Day 6: Songs of My Sexuality

61 Day 7: Self- Made Mask

69 Day 8: Soundtrack of the Present

75 Day 9: Gifts in Short

81 Day 10: Mommy Emoji's

87 Day 11: Dad-cronym

93 Day 12: Rapping with Friends

97 Day 13: Drafting my Future

103 Day 14: Cover the Truth

Express Yourself

What is a Creative Prayer Journal?

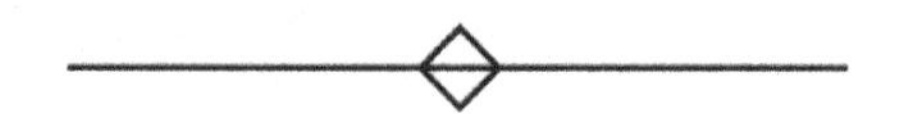

Have you ever had something to say but could not find the words to express it? So much so, that the best response that you could come up with is no response, because nothing could clearly explain what you needed to say? What if I told you not knowing how to communicate your feelings is more common than you think? Irritation, disappointment, frustration, and confusion are just a few words that we've all experienced and can be bundled up often leading to one larger emotion or feeling ... *Anger!* So many of us can express or show anger, but cannot express or communicate frustration or confusion or the feelings that brought us to that point. On the contrary, excitement, satisfaction, and approval are more positive actions and can also be bundled into one emotion – happiness. It seems so easy to show when we're happy, while other emotions and feelings can seem to get lost in translation.

This creative prayer journal will teach you ways to express your prayers to God, artistically. Although these are prayers to God, the activities will allow you to practice various creative outlets of communication that you may love and find helpful in your everyday relationships with your family and even your friends. The goal is to make you aware of the countless methods we can use to communicate expressively in prayer. And since God is the original Creator, He will understand every outlet and respond to your prayers.

"This is the confidence we have in approaching God: that if we ask anything according to his will, he hears us. And if we know that he hears us—whatever we ask—we know that we have what we asked of him."

1 John 5:14-15 AMP

So in case you were wondering, *no*, this is not your grandma's prayer journal nor is this a journal or guide that's been written and filled with those prayers you hear the intercessors in church pray - *you know the ones that seem to describe the exact issue and need of everyone in the church while using every scripture in the Bible.* No ma'am. No sir. This in fact is the opposite – in a sense. This journal has been uniquely and strategically created to give you the opportunity to find out what artistic outlet *you* can use to communicate your thoughts and to reach God for yourself. *You didn't think that was possible, huh?* Trust and know that if you seek God, you will find Him! So now, let's journey together in learning the ways you can EXPRESS YOURSELF! God is waiting to hear from you!

Before we dive deep into creative and artistic journey, I do not want to assume that everyone joining this prayer journey has given their life to Christ! Giving your life to Christ is the most important decision that you will make in life! It is more important than choosing your first job, what college you may go to, who you should be friends with, what Tik-Tok challenge is lit right now – yes, all-of-that. This decision, to make God your Lord and Savior, will change everything for you! In making such a decision, I can't guarantee you that it will make life easier, but it will give you a solid and consistent source to rely on that will guide you through all of life's experiences. In addition to this, you gain an infinite benefit - *Eternal life*! Eternal life is a life lived beyond our physical bodies and it is a life we live in Heaven with Christ. In order to become an inheritor of such a benefit, all you must do is confess your sins and believe Jesus Christ died for your sins. It's that simple! Too good to be true? Well, don't just take my word for it, take God's Word for it.

"...because if you acknowledge and confess with your mouth that Jesus is Lord {recognizing His power, authority, and majesty as God}, and believe in your heart that God raised Him from the dead, you will be saved."

Romans 10:9

You see. It *is* that simple. You may be wondering, "Well do I have to go to church and say this for it to count?" The answer is – no. The confession and declaration does not have to be done in a church or in front of a large crowd. Your confession is personal and it can be made right where you are, right now. If it is your desire to live a life of salvation, I guarantee you it will be the best decision you have ever made – but let it be a decision made from your heart. And for those who are already believers and have already made the confession of faith, it doesn't hurt to confess it again. Let's all do it together! Say these words:

God, it's me. I make mistakes every day and I am not perfect by far. Please forgive me of everything that I have done that was not good, right, or positive. I want to be different and I want to change. I want to be a new person and completely whole, even if I don't fully yet understand what that means. Please receive me. I am choosing You today! I believe that You sent Your Son, Jesus, to die for my sins. I believe that He also got up from the grave with all power, so that I may have a great life. Today I choose that great life. I choose You to be my Lord and my Savior. And I confess that at this very moment I AM SAVED!!!

I am so excited that you chose to make such an important decision today! You may not know it, but all of the angels in Heaven are partying right now because of you – *yes, you* and your decision to give your life to Christ. Now that you've taken that first step, this creative prayer journal will be a perfect addition to your life as you develop a relationship with God. Now that you're committed, let's get started!

What is prayer?

Prayer is a conversation between you and God. Over the years, you may have seen someone bow their head at the dinner table, in church, or for countless other reasons to pray. In these instances, prayer may have only seemed one-sided based on what you could physically see and audibly hear from the person you were near at the time. However, no conversation makes sense without someone responding, right?. When we pray, although we may not be able to physically see God, as we talk to Him, we must trust that He hears us and will respond to us – because He will. However, in order to hear Him, we must open our hearts and minds to hear what He is saying.

Often times, we talk to God and move on about our day. Imagine, having a friend talk to you and asks you questions but before you can respond, they get up and walk away – every-single-time? That would be annoying, right? Months can go by, and sometimes years before we realize we have been that friend – doing all of the talking – and before God can give us a response to our prayers, we get up, get dressed, walk out the door and go on about our day. Consider this *always* when in prayer. God takes the time to listen to us, so we should *make* the time to listen to Him. This is so important.

Read the following scripture aloud.

"Call to me and I will answer you and will tell you [and even show you] great and mighty things, [things which have been confined and hidden], which you do not know and understand and cannot distinguish."

Jeremiah 33:3 AMP

After reading that scripture, what does that scripture mean to you?

____

____

____

____

____

Know that God has so many things to share with you, so be sure to make time to hear from Him, and pay attention to when and how He speaks to you.

Why do we need to pray?

These two-way conversations will help you build your trust in God. The more you spend time with God, the more you will learn about Him and the stronger your relationship with Him will become. No topic is off limits and He won't' hold your faults against you when you ask for forgiveness in prayer. God freely listens, forgives, responds, teaches, and reassures with no strings attached.

So when we pray, we do so in order to become closer to God. We also pray so that we can have direction in our daily lives. God sent the Holy Spirit to live on the inside of every believer so that we would have guidance. Guidance allows us to make good decisions and helps keep our focus on the positive.

"When the Spirit of truth comes, he will guide you into all the truth, for he will not speak on his own authority, but whatever he hears he will speak, and he will declare to you the things that are to come."

John 16:13 AMP

What does that scripture mean to you?

____

____

____

____

____

____

____

____

Who is the Holy Spirit?

When we become believers, and welcome God into our lives, we also give permission for the Holy Spirit to be activated within us. The Holy Spirit is a part of the Trinity – *God the Father, God the Son and God the Holy Spirit.* They are one in the same, however, they have different functions.

"But the Helper (Comforter, Advocate, Intercessor- Counselor, Strengthener, Standby) the Holy Spirit, whom the Father will send in My name [in my place to represent Me and act on My behalf], He will teach you all things. And He will help you remember everything thing I have told you."

John 14:26 AMP

The previous scripture gives us several descriptions for the Holy Spirit. Who is the Holy Spirit to you?

____

____

____

____

There are many ways in which the "Helper" can assist us on the earth. The Holy Spirit is a spirit that guides us through life. No, we cannot see a physical being holding our hand and walking us down the street, but He is present and always desiring to speak to our spirit man. As believers, we know that what some call *"intuition"* or a *"gut feeling"* in a situation, is the Holy Spirit's hand at work. Being sensitive to the Holy Spirit will be a major part of your prayer journey. Your sensitivity to the Spirit will increase as you build a stronger relationship with God. Are you ready?

The Holy Spirit was sent after Jesus was resurrected and no longer here on earth. The Holy Spirit's purpose is to do exactly what the scripture has stated, and it will also lead you to the place(s) God needs you to go. If you ever find yourself on the wrong path, you should consult with the

Holy Spirit and find out if where you are is where God in fact wants you to be. And if not, be sensitive to the direction of the Holy Spirit as It leads you back onto the correct path.

How do I know God is speaking to me?

There is no deep mysterious voice coming from the heavens giving orders or directions. As believers we rely on the Holy Spirit to speak through God's Word, experiences and through others. We can also hear from God through our five senses. The Holy Spirit will share with you what God is saying through a smell or a texture in something you touched, or even in something you hear. In this case, the word "share" means to make you aware or understand. Often, we mistake these feelings, sounds, etc. for everyday life occurrences, but we should not. Just as God created all things, He also uses all things to speak to His children. As you grow in prayer, you will notice that there may be one specific way God speaks to you. So let's take a moment and allow you to ask God to reveal His voice to you. Say the following aloud:

God, open my senses so that I may hear, see, taste, smell, and feel You. Open my understanding to Your Word. Make Yourself plain to me. Show me who You are. Reveal Yourself to me. I am ready to receive all of You. In Jesus name, Amen.

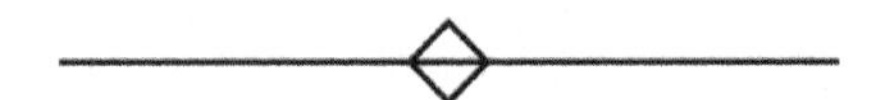

Ok, now that we have done some essential work, we can begin our creative prayer journaling. You may say, "I don't know how to pray" or, "I don't know where to start." That is a great place to be. You can develop your own journey of prayer without outside influence. There are just a few things to consider. We are not just praying to God but developing a relationship with the Father. Consider the things that you need in a relationship. God desires that and so much more. Before you start journaling, know that there are steps that can allow you to develop that relationship with God in prayer. I have listed Prayer A.C.T.S. that will become a great reference to you as you learn how to communicate with God through prayer. Read through them first and reference them as much as you need to throughout your journaling process. Ready? Let's Go!

Prayer **ACTS**

Adoration:

How does it make you feel when your parents say how much of a great job you have done on completing your chores? What about, when you finally get that report card that shows your improvement, and your parents say they are proud of you? Here is another one. When you have a bad day, and someone just says that they love you? Yea I know. You have nothing but positive emotions. It makes you want to work harder, push further, and love deeper.

That is exactly how God feels when you, His child, show gratitude by highlighting what great things He is doing through your life in prayer. God loves when we show that we appreciate Him. Every time we go to Him, adoration should be our priority. Start with your positive affection toward Him.

Example: *God, You are so awesome. When I thought I could not pass the test in English, You reminded me of every answer that seemed difficult. If I could describe it in a sentence I would say, "God, You are a present help," meaning You are right there when I need You.*

Practice: What do you love about God?

Confession:

You get those fresh Jordan's a month before school starts and your mom says, "Do not wear those shoes now, they are your school shoes." Your best friend has a back to school skate party and your mom says you can go; however, she is working late so you will have to catch a ride. You pick out your outfit and the only shoes that coordinate are those J's. Why not wear them? You take them out of the box, completing your outfit. There is a honk outside. You head to the door in a hurry, step out and lock the door. Moving briskly down the sidewalk, you trip, scuffing your new shoes. Panic is your only emotion. You try to clean it as best you can but there is still evidence. You proceed to the party and try to enjoy the evening.

A month later you are getting ready for your first day of school. You throw on your new Jordan's however this time there is an obvious scuff mark, and your mom notices it. What do you say?

Confession is telling the truth about it no matter the consequence. Not only is it worth telling, but you must also feel the wrong of your disobedience. We must tell God the truth. Yes, He already knows it, but telling Him shows you acknowledge the wrong and want to make it right. He loves us so much that no matter how bad it is, He forgives us every time. Just make sure it is coming from your heart.

Example: *God, forgive me. I had a bad day and instead of coming to You about it, I lashed out at my siblings. I know that there is a better way to deal with my emotions. I am sorry.*

Practice: God forgive me for...

Thanksgiving:

Every year in November we celebrate Thanksgiving. Many families take this time to show gratitude to their family and close friends. Their dining room tables are filled with a large turkey stuffed with dressing, collard greens, macaroni and cheese, green bean casserole, candied yams, cranberry sauce, dinner rolls and a variety of delicious, sweet desserts. The family gathers around the table and says what they are thankful for. Then, they indulge in all the food, eating until they must loosen their pants for relief. This happens once a year.

As a child of God, we know that we have something to be grateful for every single day. We do not have to wait until November to express it. Every time we pray, we are reminded of all that He has done, and we must let Him know it.

Example: *God I thank You for my mom who takes care of me as a single parent. Even when she is tired, she makes sure that I eat and have everything I need to be the best person I can be.*

Practice: What are you thankful to God for?

Supplication:

The new PS5 is scheduled to come out soon. Although you have the current game system, you really want to stay on trend. The problem is that it is expensive. It is nothing you can afford on your allowance, so you must make a choice. You can either continue using your current gaming system and save your allowance, which will take well over a year or you can ask your parents. Which one will it be? Try it on your own or ask your parents for help?

Often, we have things we want to do, but we do not know how to do it, or we do not have the resources to do it, so we go without. What if I told you that God loves doing things for His children? We just need to ask Him. But we cannot just go to Him asking for things without being obedient to what He asks of us.

Consider asking your parents for the $1,000 gaming system and you have bad grades, you talk back, and you have not done your chores. Do you think they would want to give it to you? Of course not. The consequences of our actions can prevent God from releasing gifts He already has for you. Then on the other hand, our obedient actions can persuade God to release every good gift that He has for us. Be obedient and ask God for what you want.

Example: *God, I know that You are a healer, please heal me from asthma so I can continue the sports I love without having attacks.*

Practice: Ask God to do something for you.

As you start journaling, please remember to incorporate your A.C.T.S. while writing your prayers. Every piece of art you create, use it to grow closer to God. Look for God in all that you do. Open your eyes, ears, and heart. Be patient! He is sure to respond.

Day 1

Multiple Identities

Whether we have many friends or seem to be a loner, we have an identity. We can lose ourselves in being like everyone else or not develop at all because we want to always be alone. Neither is healthy. We must recognize who created us, who we are and what our purpose is. How we identify ourselves will define how others see us and how we walk in our purpose. Surrendering to God will help us establish a healthy identity. Try it!

What are some positive thoughts I think about myself?

____

____

____

____

____

What are some negative thoughts I think about myself?

____

____

____

____

____

What Does God say about you?

Scripture reference:

"For You formed my innermost parts; You knit me [together] in my mother's womb. I will give thanks and praise to You, for I am fearfully and wonderfully made; Wonderful are Your works, and my soul knows it very well. My frame was not hidden from You, When I was being formed in secret, and intricately and skillfully formed [as if embroidered with many colors] in the depths of the earth." *Psalms 139:13-14 AMP*

What does this verse say to you?

____

____

____

____

____

Let's begin with multi-media journaling! Using what you wrote in the previous questions, now talk to God here. Write your thoughts, prayers and questions. Use these words to form your art. It is simply using various textures, objects, words, etc. to get your idea across – like creating a collage or vision board. Use magazines, newspaper, glitter, playing or sport cards and different textures to express who you are. Incorporate your likes, hobbies, and other fun facts. Be as detailed as possible. Reference your prayer A.C.T.S. on pages 16-22 if you need help to get going. Create your multi-media journal on the next page

____

____

____

____

____

Multiple Ideas / Multi-Media Collage

Day 2

Speak Poetry

There are countless ways to communicate. We often learn forms of communication through childhood experience. If we grew up in a home that showed love, spoke positive affirmations, and empowered you, we often take on these forms of communication. On the contrary, if we were raised in a toxic environment with yelling and screaming, physical and verbal abuse, or ignoring silence, we may only know that form of interaction. The goal is to give clear, and positive expressions and words of communication. No matter where you are in this area, there is always room for growth. Ready to grow? Start here!

What are some positive ways I communicate?

____

____

____

____

What are some negative ways I communicate?

____

____

What does God say about communication?

Scripture Reference:

"Let your speech at all times be gracious and pleasant, seasoned with salt, so that you will know how to answer each one {who questions you}." *Colossians 4:6 AMP*

What does this verse say to you?

There are so many different forms of poetry. Some rhyme and others, not so much. But every line communicates an emotion that the reader can feel with each word read or spoken. This journal entry makes space for you to create your own poem. It does not have to be as perfect as the great Maya Angelou, but it should be authentically you.

Try your best to step outside of your comfort zone using words and expressions that can convey the previous questions answered about communication. This poem should be at least a full page. Remember, this is a prayer journal, so we are talking to God in every activity. Your prayer A.C.T.S. are a great reference. Ready? Go!

Day 3

A Snap of the Past

Close your eyes and think about your childhood. Let each picture flash before your eyes like a photograph. Your family, friends, dreams, and disappointments. Think of it all! This should bring you great memories but may also bring some heartbreaking moments as well. Feel every emotion that your past has brought you. Take it all in. Let each photo speak to you.

Is it what you thought it should be? Let's discuss it here!

What memories of my past were good?

____

____

____

____

____

____

____

____

What memories of my past were disappointing?

____

____

____

____

____

____

____

____

What does God say about it?

Scripture Reference

"And we know [with great confidence] that God [who is deeply concerned about us] causes all things to work together [as a plan] for good for those who love God, to those who are called according to His plan and purpose." *Romans 8:28 AMP*

What does this scripture mean to you?

____

____

____

____

Okay, so here is the creative part!!! Talk to God using a method called photo journaling. Use pictures from around the house or your phone to create a journal of your thoughts. This will take some time, however as you go through old pictures it will help you share with God more in prayer. You can layer pictures in order of dates or memories on this page or a collage on your phone. Do not forget this is a prayer journal. As you reminisce, speak to God aloud on how you

felt with each memory. Also write a small description on the back of each picture to express your thoughts. He hears you!

Pic 1	Pic2	Pic 3	Pic 4
Pic 5	Pic 6	Pic 7	Pic 8
Pic 9	Pic 10	Pic 11	Pic 12

Day 4

The Mime Express

We just prayed about communication. Directly connected to communication is how we feel and how we express our emotions. How we express ourselves affect everyone around us. Yes, it is ok to have feelings. That is a healthy part of life. And yes, you need to feel every one of them. However, the actions with these feelings speak volumes. The outlet of prayer will help us with expressing ourselves the right way. Key: The Holy Spirit will help you with your expressions as you build this relationship.

What are some of my positive emotions?

____

____

____

____

What are some of my negative emotions?

____

____

____

____

What does God say about my emotions?

Scripture Reference:

"Like a city that is broken down and without walls {leaving it unprotected} Is a man who has no self-control over his spirit {and sets himself up for trouble}." *Proverbs 25:28*

What does this verse say to you?

Now talk to God by using the lines provided below. Share with Him the good, the bad, the ugly and the beautiful. Reference your prayer A.C.T.S. if you need help to get going on this page. Then, let's create!

Have you ever played Gestures? It is a game where you communicate a word without talking, using expression or body language. Mime is that in a nutshell. Our body language and expressive facial features often speak louder than our words. Look back at your prayer above. Express those drastic emotions with facial expressions, and body language, releasing every unhealthy form of communication.

What Expressions did you use? Draw them here! Use as much detail as possible!

Day 5

The Mental Picture

Depression, anxiety, and suicide are just a few emotions associated with mental health. These emotions are more common than you think, but are often pushed aside because of denial, shame, or pride. It is important to deal with these thoughts so that we can overcome them and help someone else dealing with the same thoughts. Just like the art of painting, the state of our mental health can be overlooked even when it is screaming loud with purpose.

What thoughts/emotions have I embraced?

____

____

____

____

What thoughts/emotions have I suppressed?

____

____

____

____

What does the Bible say? (Multiple references are added for additional support).

Scripture Reference:

"...casting all your cares {all your anxieties, all your worries, and all your concerns, once and for all} on Him, for He cares about you {with deepest affection, and watches over you very carefully}." *1 Peter 5:7 AMP*

What does this verse say to you?

____

____

____

____

____

____

____

____

____

Additional Scripture References:

"And the peace of God {that peace that reassures the heart, that peace} which transcends all understanding, {that peace which} stands guard over your heart and your minds in Christ {is yours}. Finally, believers, whatever is true, whatever is honorable and worthy of respect, whatever is right and confirmed by God's word, whatever is lovely and brings peace, whatever is admirable and of good repute; if there is any excellence, if there is any worthy of praise, think continually on these things {center your mind on them, and implant them in your heart}." *Philippians 4:7-8 AMP*

"For God did not give us a spirit of timidity or cowardice or fear, but {He has given us a spirit} of power and of love and of sound judgement and personal discipline {abilities that result in a calm, well- balanced mind and self- control." *2 Timothy 1:7 AMP*

This is not an easy subject. Talking to God can help you understand more about yourself. Spend time reviewing the answers to the previous questions. Close your eyes and visualize the transition between what you think of yourself and what God sees in you.

Try it again. Read your answers, then close your eyes and picture the transition. Got it? Great! Now, follow your prayer A.C.T.S. and talk to God about it.

Okay, now it is your turn to try your hand at a masterpiece. Try painting or drawing an intricate artistic expression of the state of your mental health and where it is going as you continue building a relationship with God through prayer. The next two pages will be a *before-and-after* **mural**. Do not rush this process. Take your time on the details and meditate on your answers and the scripture reference. Continue to close your eyes to visualize your art until it is completed. You've got this!

Day 6

Songs of My Sexuality

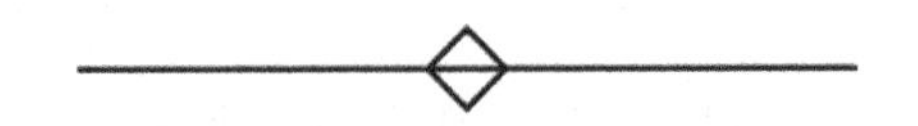

Today, acceptance is one of the most sawt after affirmations; it is also at the forefront. Your attractions, preferences and actions should all be filtered through the Holy Spirit and the Word of God. We should have self-control, including control over our sexuality. Whether you are dealing with gender identity issues, sexual thoughts and actions or pornography addiction, the Holy Spirit can guide you to where God desires you to be. This is a part of surrendering all of yourself to God. Answer the following questions and let's give God our all!

What sexual desires do I have control over?

____

____

____

____

What sexual desires do I not have control over?

____

____

____

____

What does God say about me?

Scripture Reference:

"No temptation [regardless of its source] has overtaken or enticed you that is not common to human experience [nor is any temptation unusual or beyond human resistance]; but God is faithful [to His word—He is compassionate and trustworthy], and He will not let you be tempted beyond your ability [to resist], but along with the temptation He [has in the past and is now and] will [always] provide the way out as well, so that you will be able to endure it [without yielding, and will overcome temptation with joy]. " *I Corinthians 10:13 AMP*

What does this verse say to me?

____

____

____

____

Now that we have identified our sexual identity to God, let's submit our prayers through song. Write a song that discusses the struggle you have written about above and your submission of them to God. At minimum, write two verses and a course. Feel free to write more. – it's all according to what you need to talk to God about. Ready? Set! Pray!

Title

____

Verse 1

____

____

Chorus

Verse 2

Chorus

Day 7

Self-Made Mask

Often, we are posing as two different people. We are one way in one environment and different in another. It is usually because there are parts of us that we want to hide. We mask those feelings behind big smiles, a fly wardrobe, and a pleasant personality or with aggressive behavior, and creative slang. But what if we could address our insecurities and become comfortable with being who we truly are? Let us believe what God says about us.

What am I confident in?

____

____

____

____

What am I insecure in?

____

____

____

____

What does God say about me?

Scripture Reference:

"You can't keep your true self hidden forever; before long you will be exposed."

- *Luke 12:2 MSG*

What does this verse mean to me?

____

____

____

____

Unmask yourself and discuss the ugly things with God. He accepts all of you, just how you are. Exposing the hidden areas of our life are important. It is the only way that we can address them. Write them down and ask God to help you and be truthful with yourself. Continue to use your prayer A.C.T.S. for this journal.

____

____

____

____

____

____

____

____

____

____

On the next two pages you will cut out and decorate two different masks. The first mask represents the person you portray to everyone, hiding those insecurities that you discussed. The second mask is sharing the way God sees you. Be thorough in your creativity. When you are done put the second mask on in the mirror, showcasing what God says about you. Take a picture in each mask, and recite this scripture:

> "I praise you because I am fearfully and wonderfully made; your works are wonderful; I know that full well." *Psalms 139:14 NIV*

Day 8

Soundtrack of the Present

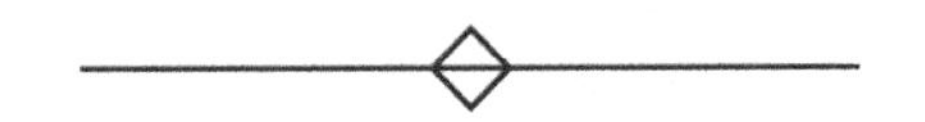

Today is a new day!!! It is up to you to determine how it will go! Often, we think of our past and our future and forget about what is going on now. Here is an opportunity for you to share with God how you feel in this moment. How can God help you in this moment? It may be in school, work, family, or anything but God wants to hear it.

What things are going well for me now?

____

____

____

____

____

____

____

____

What things are not going well for me?

____

____

____

____

What does God say about it?

Scripture Reference:

"Do not remember the former things or ponder the things of the past. Listen carefully, I am about to do a new thing, now it will spring forth; Will you not be aware of it? I will even put a road in the wilderness, Rivers in the desert." *Isaiah 43:18-19*

What does this scripture say to you?

Music and beats have an important role in every culture. The rhythm, the volume, and the instrument are all tools to get the listener to feel a thought, emotion, or truth. In that movie you watched recently, did you notice the suspension of sound or music that increased in volume or tempo? Consider those movie plots and how the music played a major role in drawing you into the story. Your story is even more powerful. What will be your soundtrack for your life right now? Use your phone, a beat machine, or get some pots and pans if you must. Create a sound that would translate your prayers to God.

Write your prayers to God below by using your prayer A.C.T.S. to express what concerns you right now. Then get to creating that sound! Be sure to listen to His response.

Day 9

Gifts in Short

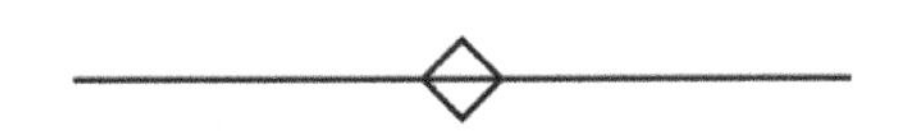

What are your gifts? Not just those neatly wrapped boxes with large red bows that we get on our birthday or during Christmas. These gifts are abilities or talents that may come naturally, or we have practiced at something enough to become great at it. God gave you all those abilities that you possess. If you think long enough, there are bound to be some things that you can do well that would surprise even yourself.

What am I good at?

____

____

____

____

What am I terrible at?

____

____

____

____

What does God say I can do?

Scripture Reference:

"I can do all things {which He has called me to do} through Him, who strengthens and empowers me {to fulfill His purpose—I am self- sufficient in Christ's sufficiency; I am ready for anything and equal to anything through Him who infuses me with inner strength and confident peace.}" *Philippians 4:13 AMP*

What does this verse say to you?

____

____

____

____

Have you ever read a story in a magazine or an online blog, about a page long, with small font, with so much information that you had to read it twice, just to ensure you understood it all? Well, writing short stories is an art. Use this section to create a short story, article, or blog. Use your prayers as inspiration. Do not forget your A.C.T.S. reference.

____

____

____

____

____

____

____

____

____

____

Day 10

Mommy Emoji's

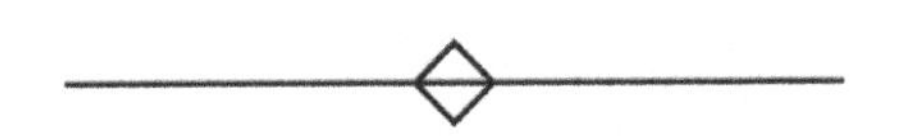

We all have different relationships with our moms, however God allowed us to be birthed from them for a reason. Whether the relationship is a good one or non- existent, let's acknowledge their presence (or lack of) in our lives. How has your mom made you who you are? If you have a great relationship, what areas can make it *even* better. If the relationship is less than desirable, what areas need to be restored (fixed)? Are you ready to do some hard work? Okay, Go!

What are some positive thoughts you think about your mom? It may be challenging for you to complete this task if your mom isn't present in your life, so if she's not, that's okay. Instead answer, what are some positive ways you think your mom being in your life would impact you?

____

____

____

____

____

What are some negative thoughts you think about your mom?

____

____

____

What Does God say?

Scripture reference:

"Honor [esteem, value as precious] your father and your mother [and be respectful to them]—this is the first commandment with a promise— 3so that it may be well with you, and that you may have a long life on the earth." - Ephesians 6:2-3 AMP

What does this verse say to you?

Let's use some creative coding. Today you will journal using as many emojis as you can. And yes, you can use some words and you can create your own emojis. Using what you wrote in the previous questions, now talk to God. Reference your prayer A.C.T.S. if you need help to get going.

Day 11

Dad-cronym

Our fathers play a significant role in our lives. Whether they are present or we have never seen them before, either reality impacts our lives drastically. When the relationship with our father is strong, we may often feel a sense of security and can thrive, however when the relationship is weak or non-existent, it can be devastating. Share your thoughts with God today.

What are some positive thoughts you think about your dad? It may be challenging for you to complete this task if your dad isn't present in your life, so if he's not, that's okay. Instead answer, what are some positive ways you think your dad being in your life would impact you?

____

____

____

____

____

What are some negative thoughts you think about your dad (whether present or absent)?

____

____

____

What does God say about a father?

Scripture reference:

"He will turn the hearts of the fathers to their children, and the hearts of the children to their fathers [a reconciliation produced by repentance] ..."

Malachi 4:6

What does this scripture say to you?

In this journal entry you will use only acronyms. What is an acronym? An acronym is an abbreviation of a word or words. The common "LOL" acronym is an example. We all know that means to do what? ________________________! Yes, you are correct, Laugh Out Loud. Your entire journal entry will be acronyms. Got it? Great! Let's began acronym journaling! Using what you wrote in the previous questions, now talk to God. Reference your Prayer A.C.T.S. for assistance.

Day 12

Rapping with Friends

Friendships can be complicated. You would be blessed to find *one* friend that can stand the test of time. Many times, we get caught in the quantity of (how many) friends we have versus focusing on the quality of our friendships. Having quality friendships would produce the kinds of friends who may not always tell you what you want to hear, but will always say what you need to hear --- for your betterment. Love and respect are also important. Yes, you will have many friends along the way as you grow and mature, however not all friendships are meant to last. Guess what though? That is ok! When friendships end, do not be upset. Every form of growth requires some kind of shedding – so when it ends, just conclude that you both may be growing, but in different directions. You cannot take everyone with you on your journey! And again, this is okay!

Advice: choose to end all friendships on good terms. Be mature and grateful for the time you shared with that individual. Remember it was your choice to be their friend. Do not be upset with someone because of your choice or even their choice to walk away from the friendship. God will replace that friendship with someone who fits who you are becoming and where you are going. Always remember that!

So now let's talk about it!

What are some positive thoughts about my friends?

____

____

____

____

What are some negative thoughts about my friends?

____

____

____

____

What does God say about friends?

Scripture Reference

"The man of too many friends [chosen indiscriminately] will be broken in pieces and come to ruin, but there is a [true, loving] friend who [is reliable and] sticks closer than a brother." - *Proverbs 18:24 AMP*

What does this verse mean to you?

____

____

____

____

So now, this is your time to spit some FIYA bars! Do not be intimidated by the term "Rap." Rap is a form of poetry; did you know that? So yes, some of your favorite rappers are considered to be "lyricists" or "poets." And now it's your turn! The goal is to create a song with two verses and a hook. Discuss in this prayer how you see your friendships now and what decisions you will make in the future. Remember this is a prayer. Check your Prayer A.C.T.S. to help with the structure. Oh, and remember, have some fun!!!

Verse 1

Chorus

Verse 2

Chorus

Did you think that was it? One more thing! Create a dance to your hook! Think Tic Tok!!

Ready? Go!

Day 13

Drafting My future

Each of us have a past to remember and a story to tell. Our memories can be beautiful, and sometimes even devastating. Either way, there is nothing we can change about it. Our experiences leave permanent memories of what has helped shape who we are today. No matter the outcome of our pasts – whether good or bad, we cannot live there. Regardless of how good things may be or how bad we may feel things are, we can always create a better future. We determine what our future looks like by the decision that we make today. What do you want your new memories to be? Whether choosing that new school, job, relationship, partnership or building a stronger relationship with God, you can control the outcome. Start here!

What am I excited about in my future?

____

____

____

____

____

____

What am I afraid of in my future?

____

____

____

____

What does God say about it?

Scripture Reference

For I know the plans and thoughts that I have for you,' says the Lord, 'plans for peace and well-being and not for disaster, to give you a future and a hope.

-Jeremiah 29:11 AMP

What does this verse mean to you?

____

____

____

____

Now take a moment and look at your life as a building or structure. Buildings have doors, windows, rooms, stairs, elevators, walls, floors, ceilings, etc. Each component has an important job in keeping the structure standing. This is true for the areas in our lives. What are those main areas that you believe keeps or will keep your life structured?

On the next page you will create what you see your future to be in architecture form. Yes, you will create a building that represents what your future will be. Each room can be an area of importance and everything within this structure needs to have a purpose. If it does not have a purpose, we don't want it in our building. Label what you can and if you need to make an answer key, do so.

Now let's pray over your future! Ask God to show you those areas that you made rooms for and what areas we need to perform renovations! Reflect on your Prayer A.C.T.S. and use your blueprint to assist you.

Day 14

Cover the Truth

Let's review our key scriptures from the last 13 days. May these scriptures serve as simple reminders of what God's Word says about us. As you read each verse, reflect on the transformation from how you saw yourself before each day to the TRUTH. The Truth is simply what God says about you and your situation. Remind yourself of the work you have done to be all that God has called you to be within the last two weeks. We will get creative right after.

Day 1:

"For You formed my innermost parts; You knit me [together] in my mother's womb. I will give thanks and praise to You, for I am fearfully and wonderfully made; Wonderful are Your works, and my soul knows it very well. My frame was not hidden from You, When I was being formed in secret, and intricately and skillfully formed [as if embroidered with many colors] in the depths of the earth." - ***Psalms 139:13-14 AMP***

Day 2:

"Let your speech at all times be gracious and pleasant, seasoned with salt, so that you will know how to answer each one {who questions you}." - ***Colossians 4:6 AMP***

Day 3:

"And we know [with great confidence] that God [who is deeply concerned about us] causes all things to work together [as a plan] for good for those who love God, to those who are called according to His plan and purpose." - ***Romans 8:28 AMP***

Day 4:

"Like a city that is broken down and without walls {leaving it unprotected} Is a man who has no self-control over his spirit {and sets himself up for trouble}."- **Proverbs 25:28 AMP**

Day 5:

"...casting all your cares {all your anxieties, all your worries, and all your concerns, once and for all} on Him, for He cares about you {with deepest affection, and watches over you very carefully}."
- ***1 Peter 5:7 AMP***

Day 6:

"No temptation [regardless of its source] has overtaken or enticed you that is not common to human experience [nor is any temptation unusual or beyond human resistance]; but God is faithful [to His word—He is compassionate and trustworthy], and He will not let you be tempted beyond your ability [to resist], but along with the temptation He [has in the past and is now and] will [always] provide the way out as well, so that you will be able to endure it [without yielding, and will overcome temptation with joy]. "- ***I Corinthians 10:13 AMP***

Day 7:

"You can't keep your true self hidden forever; before long you will be exposed." - **Luke 12:2 MSG**

Day 8:

"Do not remember the former things or ponder the things of the past. Listen carefully, I am about to do a new thing, now it will spring forth; Will you not be aware of it? I will even put a road in the wilderness, Rivers in the desert." - ***Isaiah 43:18-19 AMP***

Day 9:

"I can do all things {which He has called me to do} through Hi, who strengthens and empowers me {to fulfill His purpose—I am self- sufficient in Christ's sufficiency; I am ready for anything and equal to anything through Him who infuses me with inner strength and confident peace.}

"He will turn the hearts of the fathers to their children, and the hearts of the children to their fathers [a reconciliation produced by repentance] ..." - ***Malachi 4:6 AMP***

Day 10:

"Honor [esteem, value as precious] your father and your mother [and be respectful to them]—this is the first commandment with a promise— 3so that it may be well with you, and that you may have a long life on the earth." - ***Ephesians 6:2-3 AMP***

Day 11:

"He will turn the hearts of the fathers to their children, and the hearts of the children to their fathers [a reconciliation produced by repentance] ..." - ***Malachi 4:6 AMP***

Day 12:

"The man of too many friends [chosen indiscriminately] will be broken in pieces and come to ruin, but there is a [true, loving] friend who [is reliable and] sticks closer than a brother."

- Proverbs 18:24 AMP

Day 13:

"For I know the plans and thoughts that I have for you,' says the Lord, 'plans for peace and well-being and not for disaster, to give you a future and a hope." - ***Jeremiah 29:11 AMP***

Wow!! You have come a long way!! God has created such an amazing person in you. Your willingness to confront the darkest places of your life and face them in prayer, is nothing short of incredible. Let's not forget challenging your creativity in new ways to express those prayers to God. I told you this is not your Grandma's prayer journal. This was specifically designed for you to show you how you can speak to God creatively. But wait!!! We must finish strong.

This last creative prayer will sum up your entire two-week journey. We are merely showing God who He has created and called us to be by saying thank you for revealing to us through His word, and in prayer, the truth about ourselves. So, what's the task? We are creating a magazine cover! What should your headline be? Look back at some of your breakthrough moments! What will be in this magazine? Articles? Blogs? Products? Advertisements? Pictures? Tell us who you are?

When you are done, hang this on your vision board, bedroom wall, office, or anywhere that you can be reminded of who you are, daily.

Express Yourself!

EXPRESS YOURSELF

Magazine

14 Days of Creative Prayer

Featuring

Add a subheading

Add a subheading

Add a subheading

Made in the USA
Coppell, TX
10 May 2022